Biff and Wilma went to the pantomime. They went with Wilma's mum. They had a friend called Anneena. Anneena went to the pantomime with them.

1

The pantomime was about Robin Hood. Robin Hood was a good man. He lived in a wood with his friends. Everyone liked Robin Hood and they gave a cheer every time he came in.

There was a bad man called the Sheriff.
Nobody liked the Sheriff. He wanted to
catch Robin Hood and lock him up.

"Look out, Robin!" shouted the children.

The next day, Wilma and Anneena went to play with Biff. They sang a song about Robin Hood. Wilma played her guitar and Anneena played her recorder.

Kipper didn't like the song. He put his
hands over his ears and made a face.
"Woooooooh," said Kipper.

Kipper had a key round his neck. It was
the magic key. Biff was cross with Kipper.
"Put the key back in the box," she said.

Suddenly the key began to glow.

"Look out, Anneena," said Biff. "This is a magic key and the magic is working. It's time for an adventure."

The magic took the children to a wood.
It was the wood where Robin Hood lived.
The children could see Robin with some of
his friends.

Robin Hood had not seen the children. Anneena was frightened.

"I hope he *is* a good man," she said.

"Come on," said Kipper. "I can smell food."

Robin Hood saw the children.
"Who are you?" he asked. "Are you lost
in the woods? Come and sit down."

The children sat by the fire.

"We saw you in a play," said Anneena. "We can sing a song about you."

"Oh no!" said Kipper. "Not the song again."

Biff, Wilma and Anneena sang the song.
The song said everyone liked Robin but
nobody liked the Sheriff. Robin Hood's
friends gave a cheer.

"What a good song!" said Robin Hood.
"Sing it to me again."
Kipper looked inside a big black pot.
Nobody saw the Sheriff coming.

Suddenly the Sheriff's men ran in. They grabbed Robin Hood and put a rope round him.

"Got you at last!" said the Sheriff.

They jumped on Robin's friends and
they grabbed Biff, Wilma, and Anneena.
They put them all into a cart.
"Take them away!" said the Sheriff.

Kipper hid in the big black pot. The
Sheriff's men didn't see him.

"Oh no!" he said. "What can I do? I
must help them."

The Sheriff took them to a village. He said, "My castle is too far away, so we will stop here. One of my men will see you don't get away."

Kipper went up to the man. He gave the
man a sweet.

"What is that thing?" he asked.

"You lock people up in it," said the man.

"You can't lock people in that," said
Kipper. "You can't get them in."

"Oh yes you can," said the man. "Look."
He put in his head and his hands.

"Ha!" said Kipper. "You fell for it."
He locked the man in and took away his
keys.

"Grrr!" said the man.

Kipper set them free.

"Come on, everyone," said Robin Hood. "Let's go back to the woods. We don't want the Sheriff to catch us."

They went to a new part of the woods.

"Three cheers for Kipper," said Robin
Hood. "Now let's sing that song about me
again."

"Oh no!" said Kipper.

Suddenly the magic key began to glow.

"Just in time," said Kipper. "It's time for us to go."

"Goodbye," said the children.

"Goodbye," said Robin Hood, "and thanks."

"What an adventure!" said Anneena. "I liked Robin Hood and his friends. Let's sing the song."

"Aaaaaah!" said Kipper.